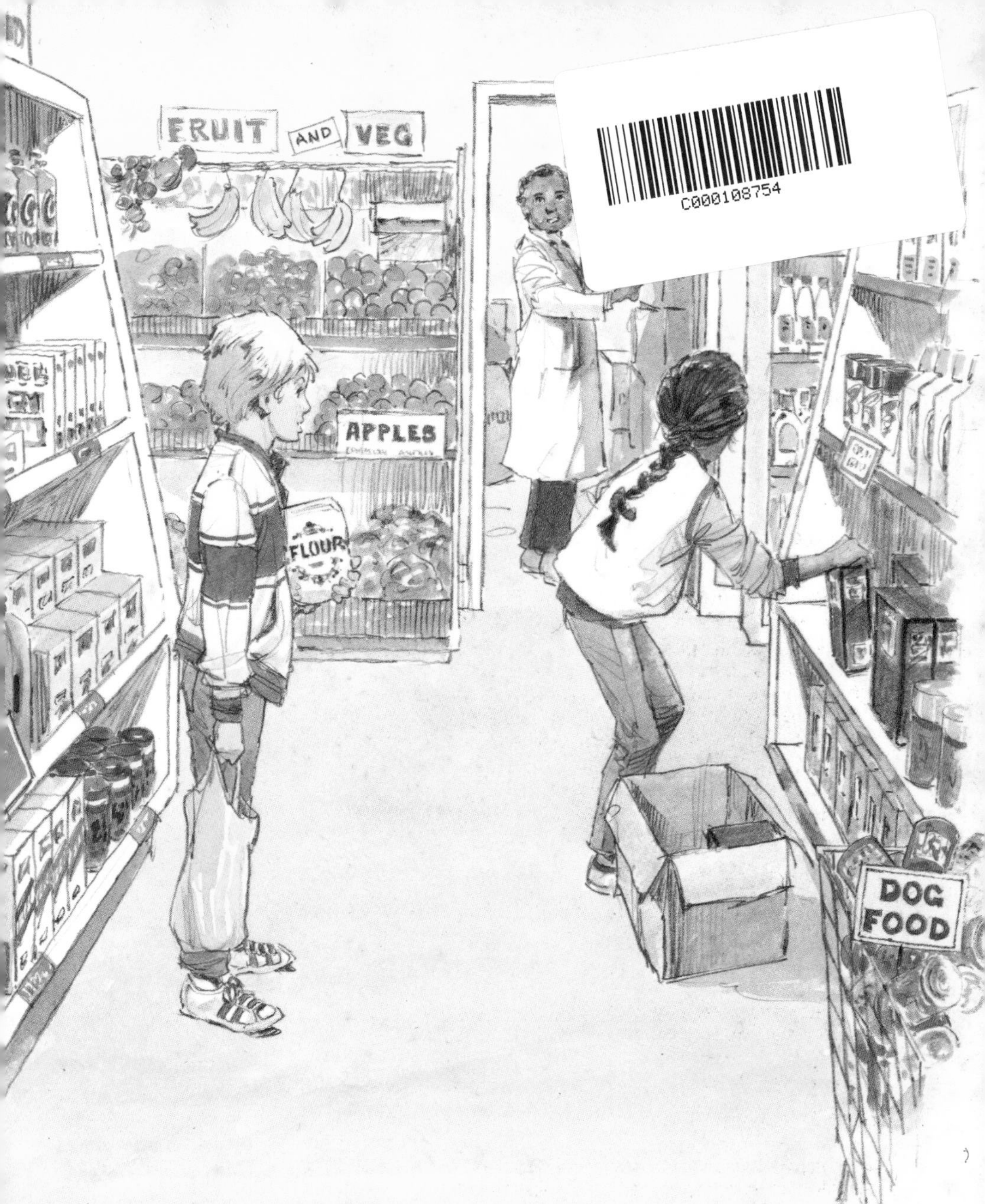
FRUIT
AND
VEG
APPLES
FLOUR
DOG FOOD

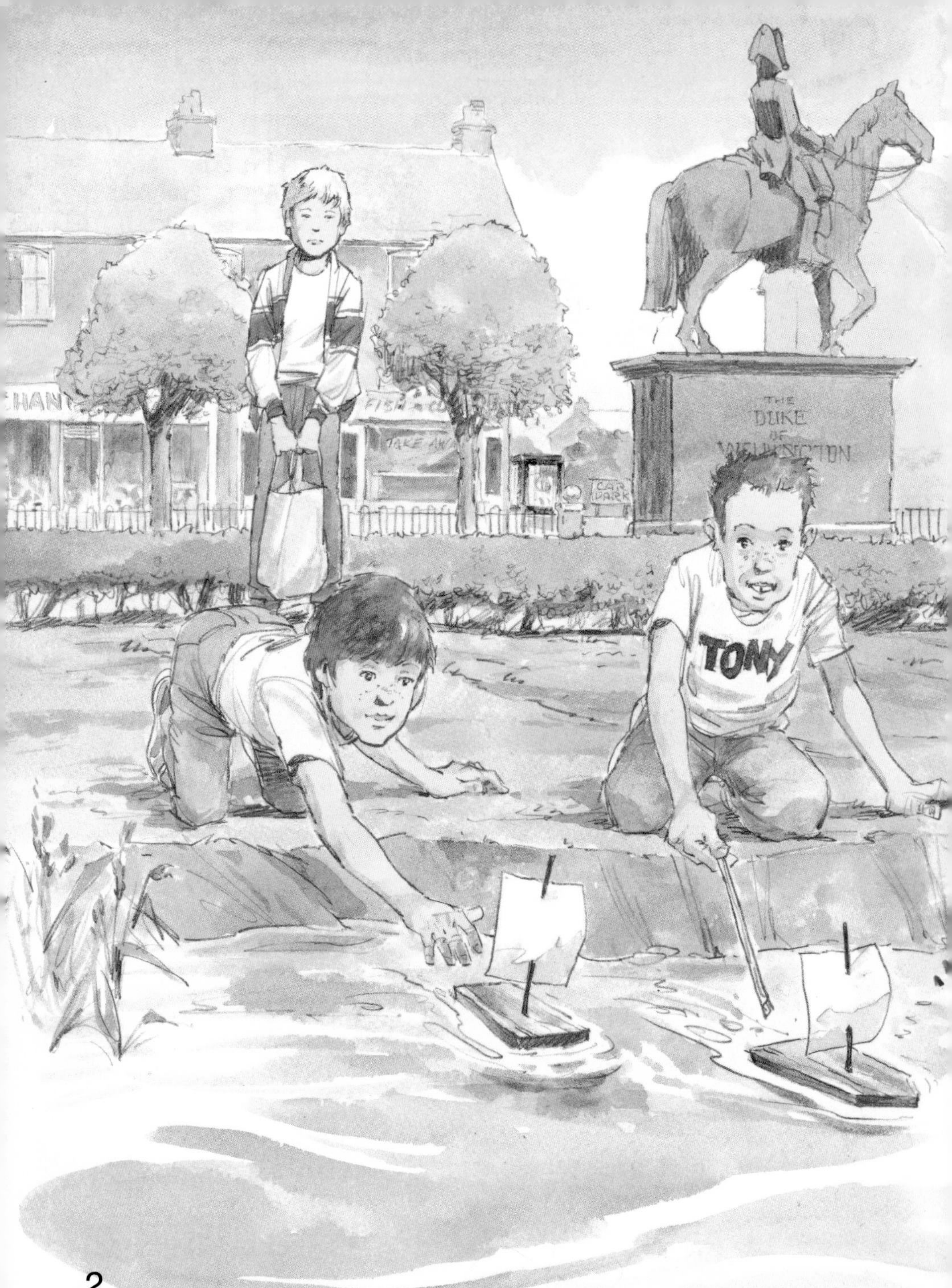
THE
DUKE
OF
TONY

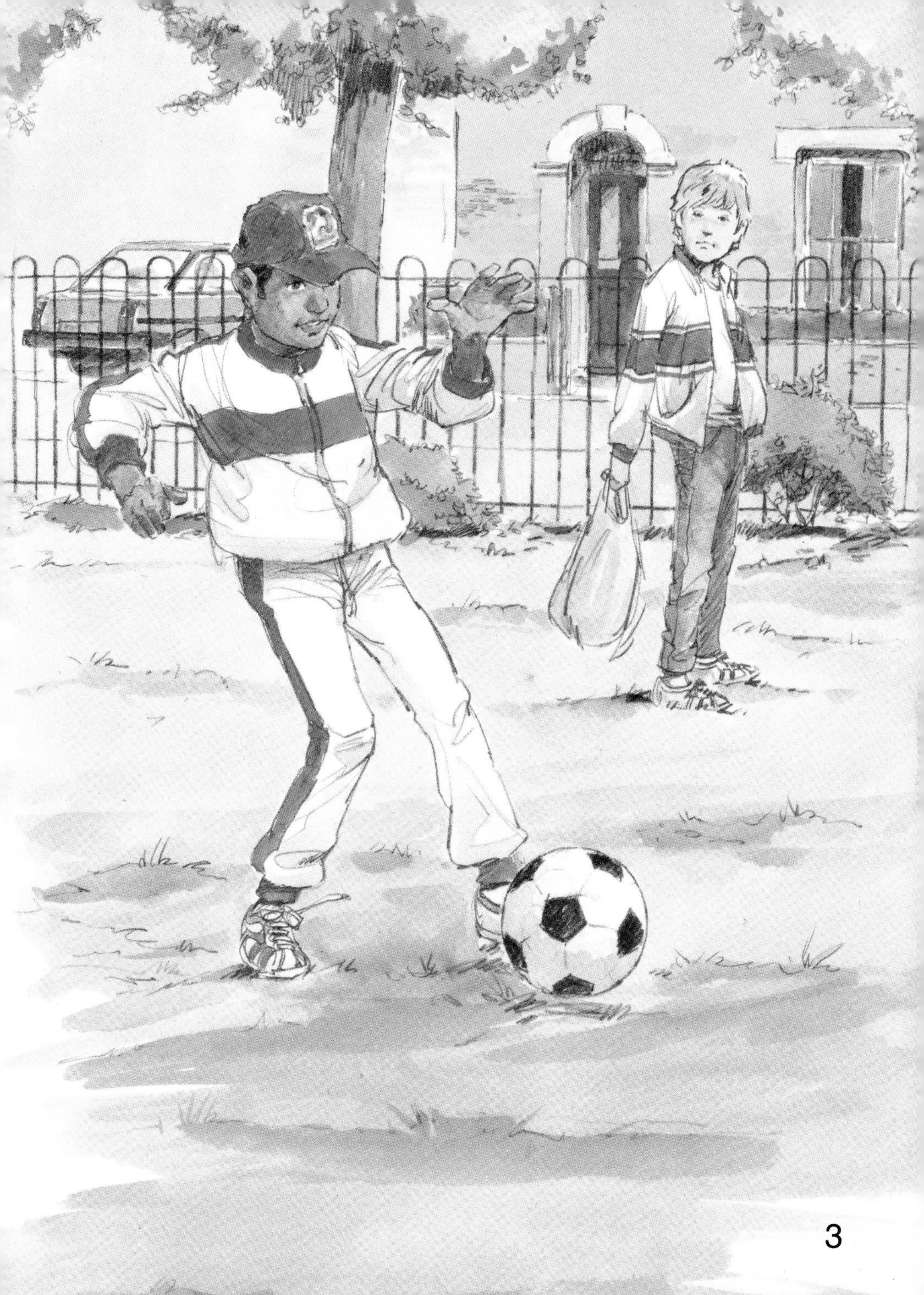

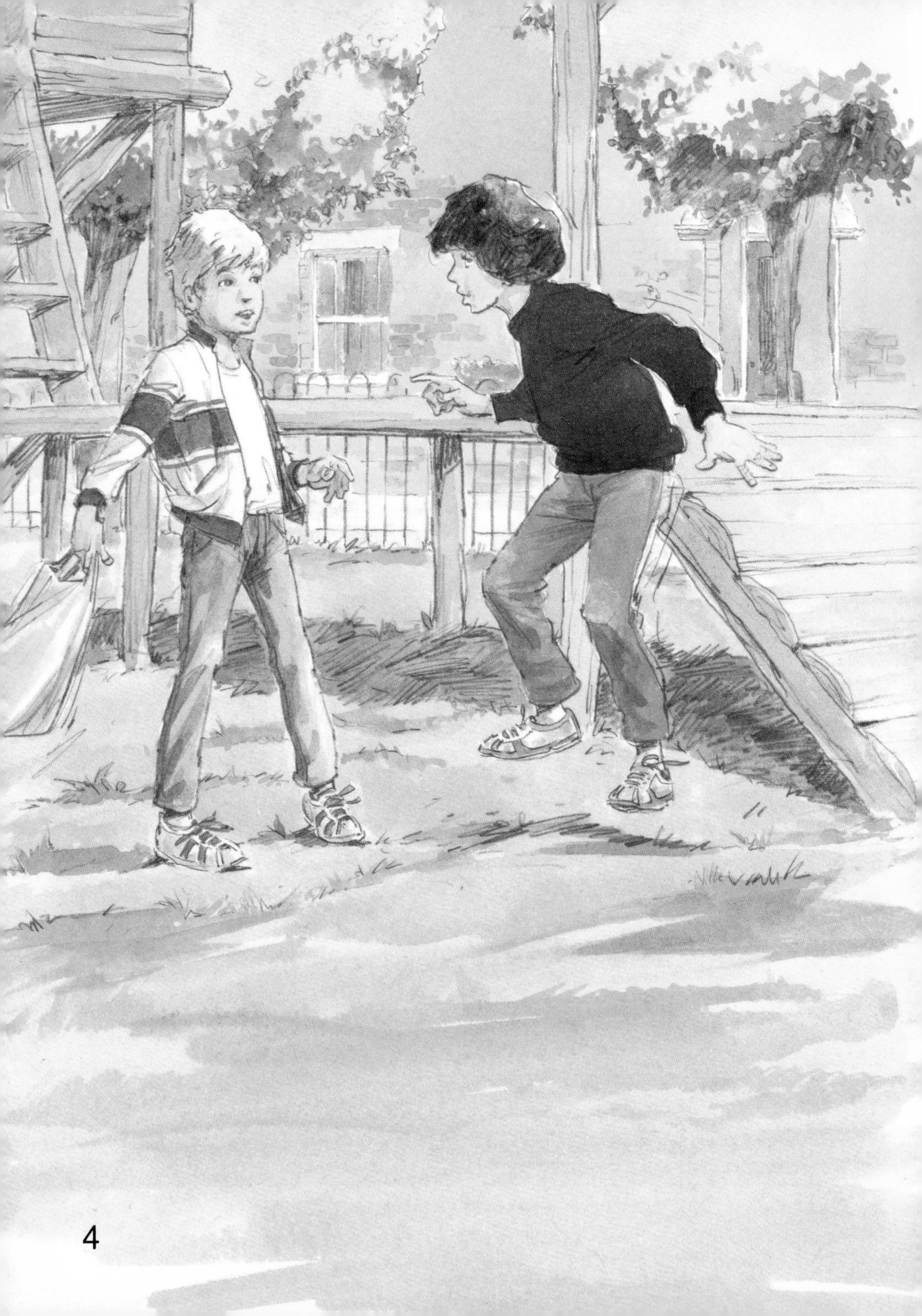

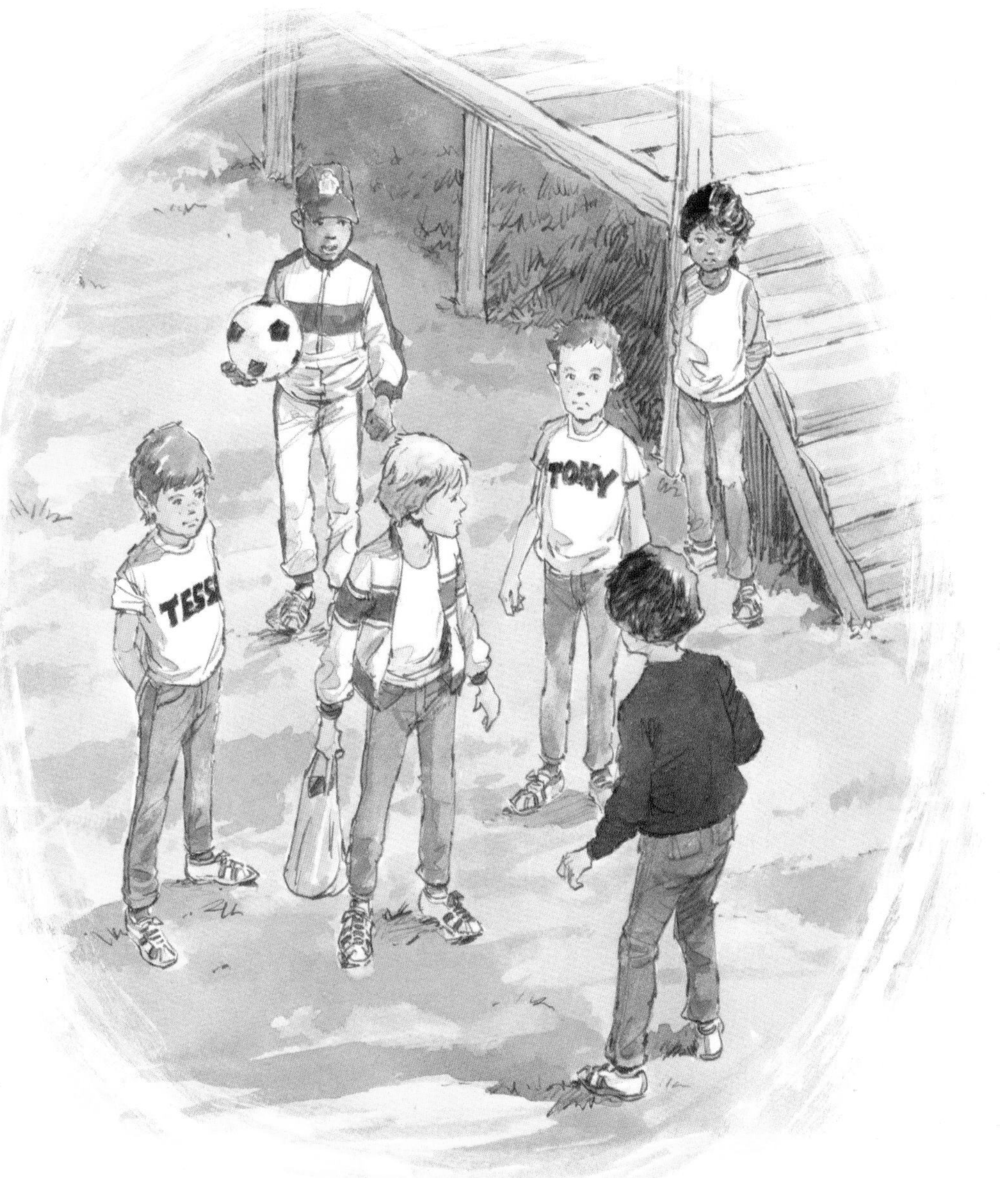
TESS
TONY

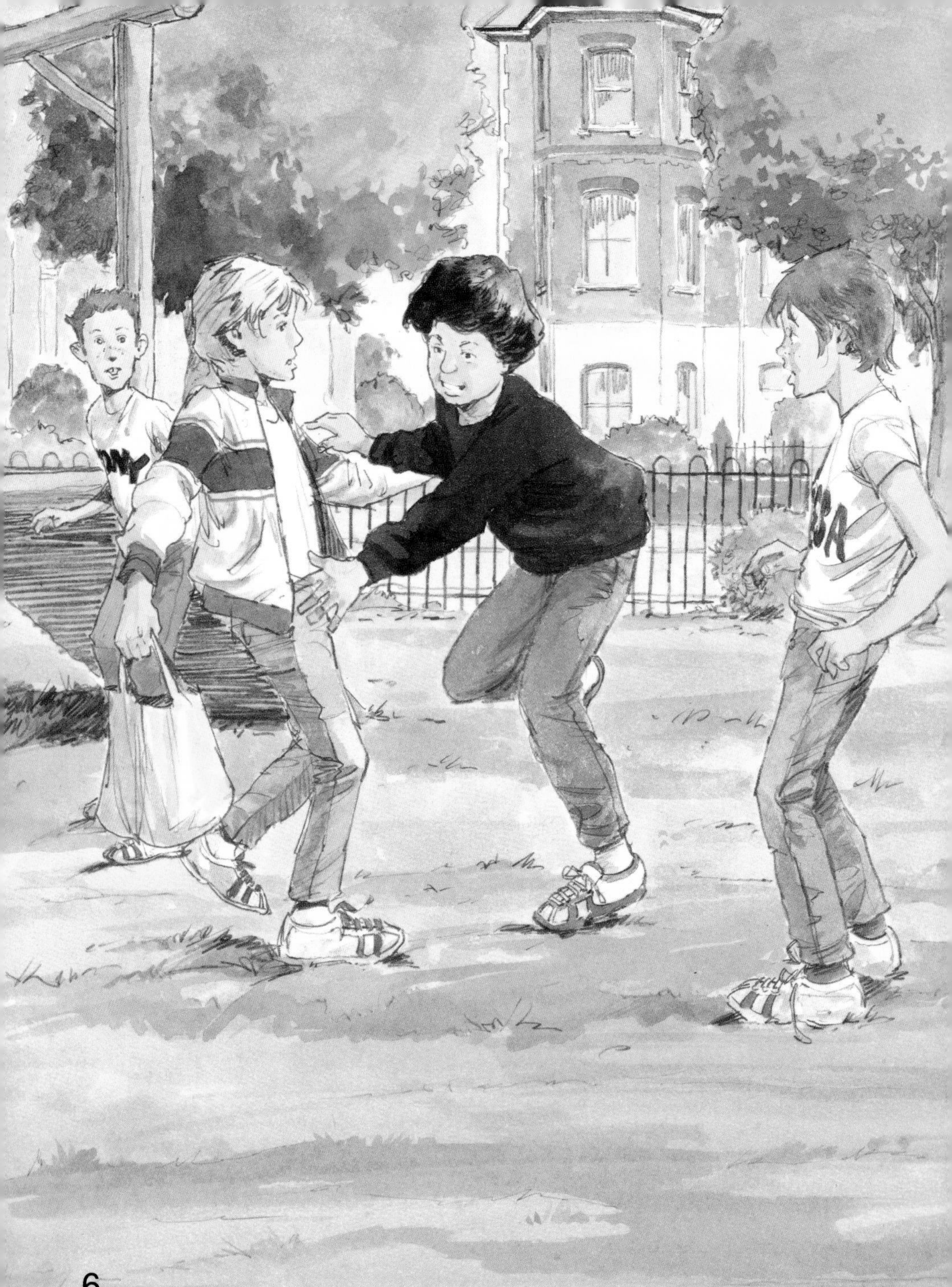

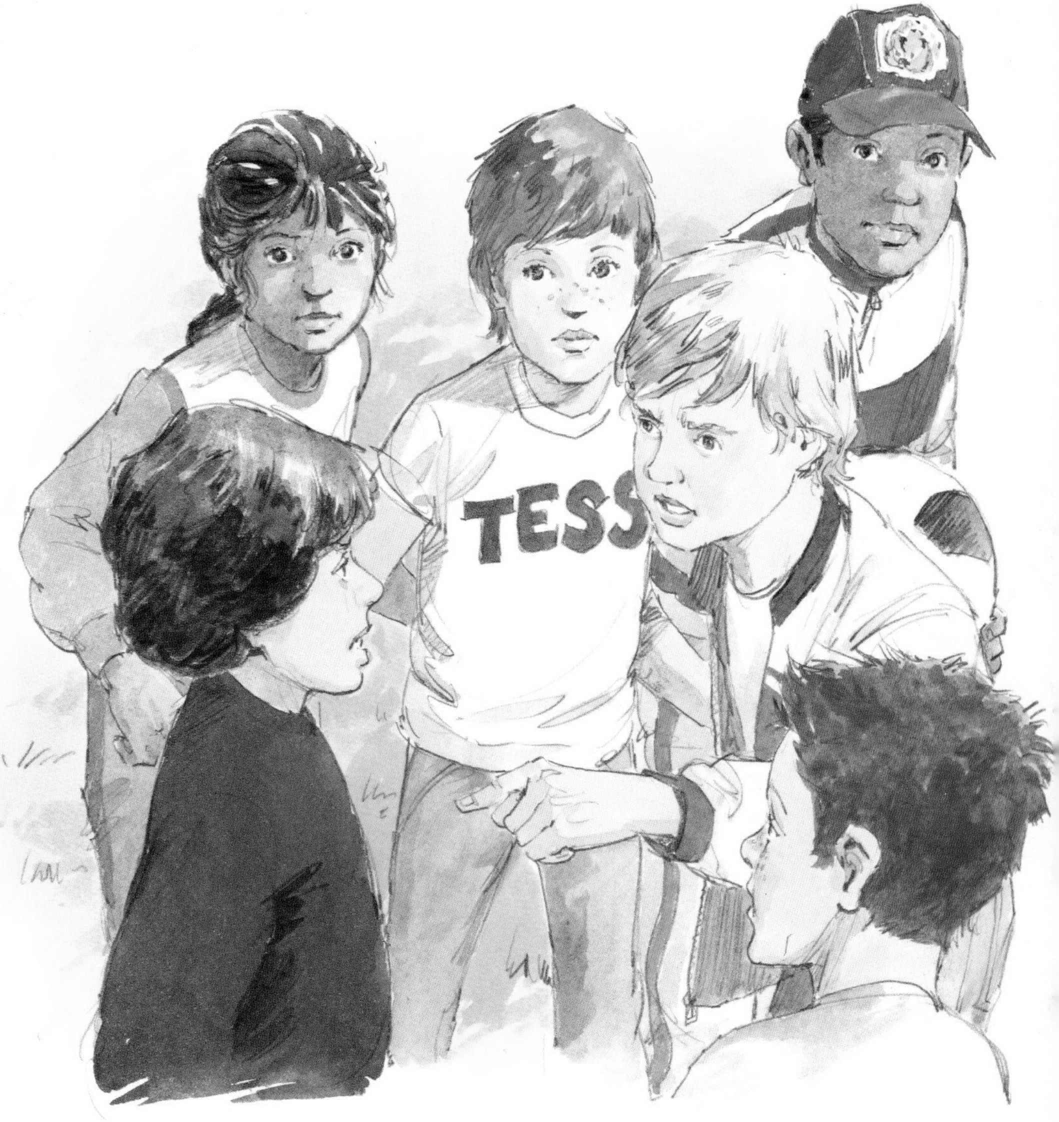
TESS

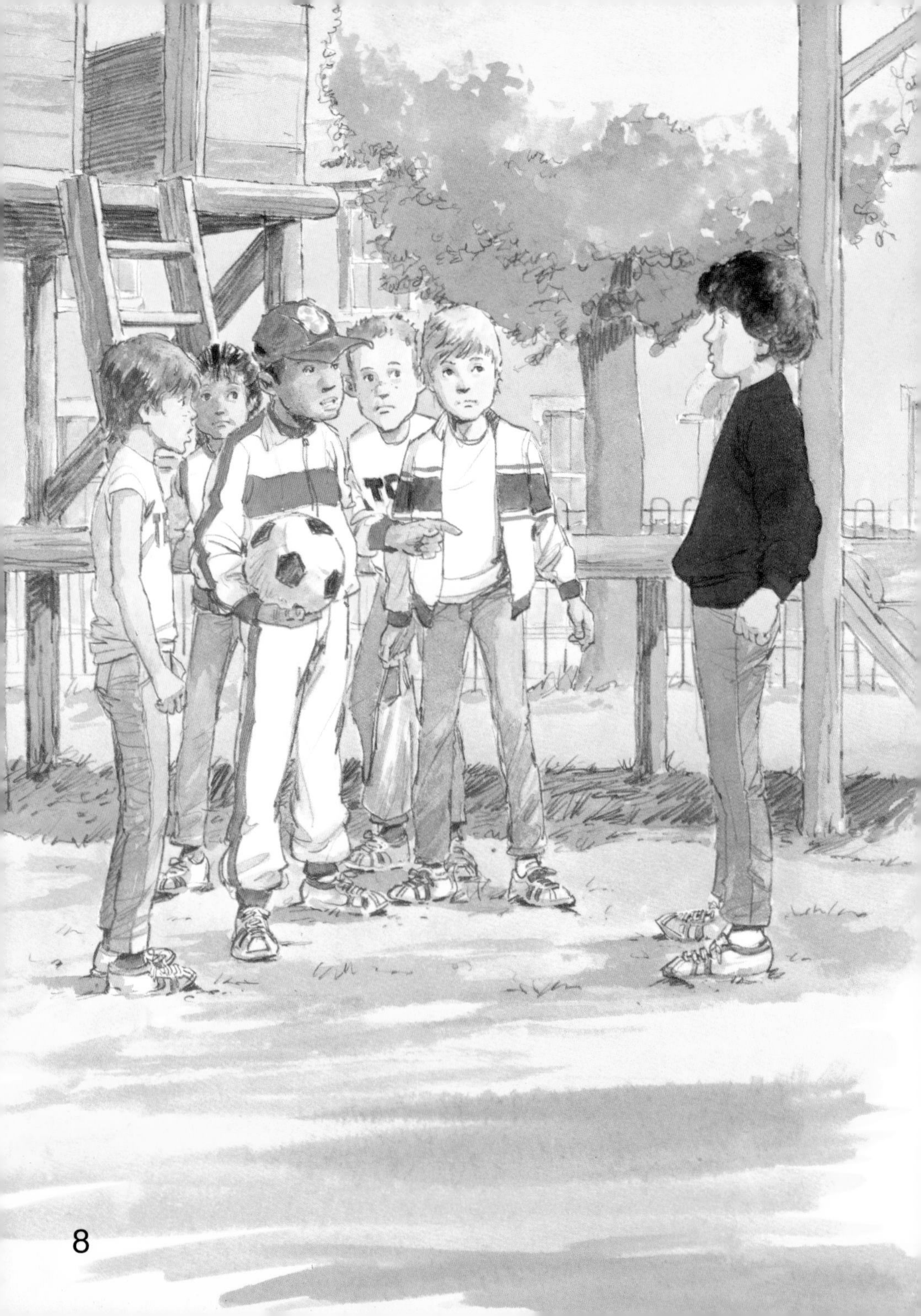

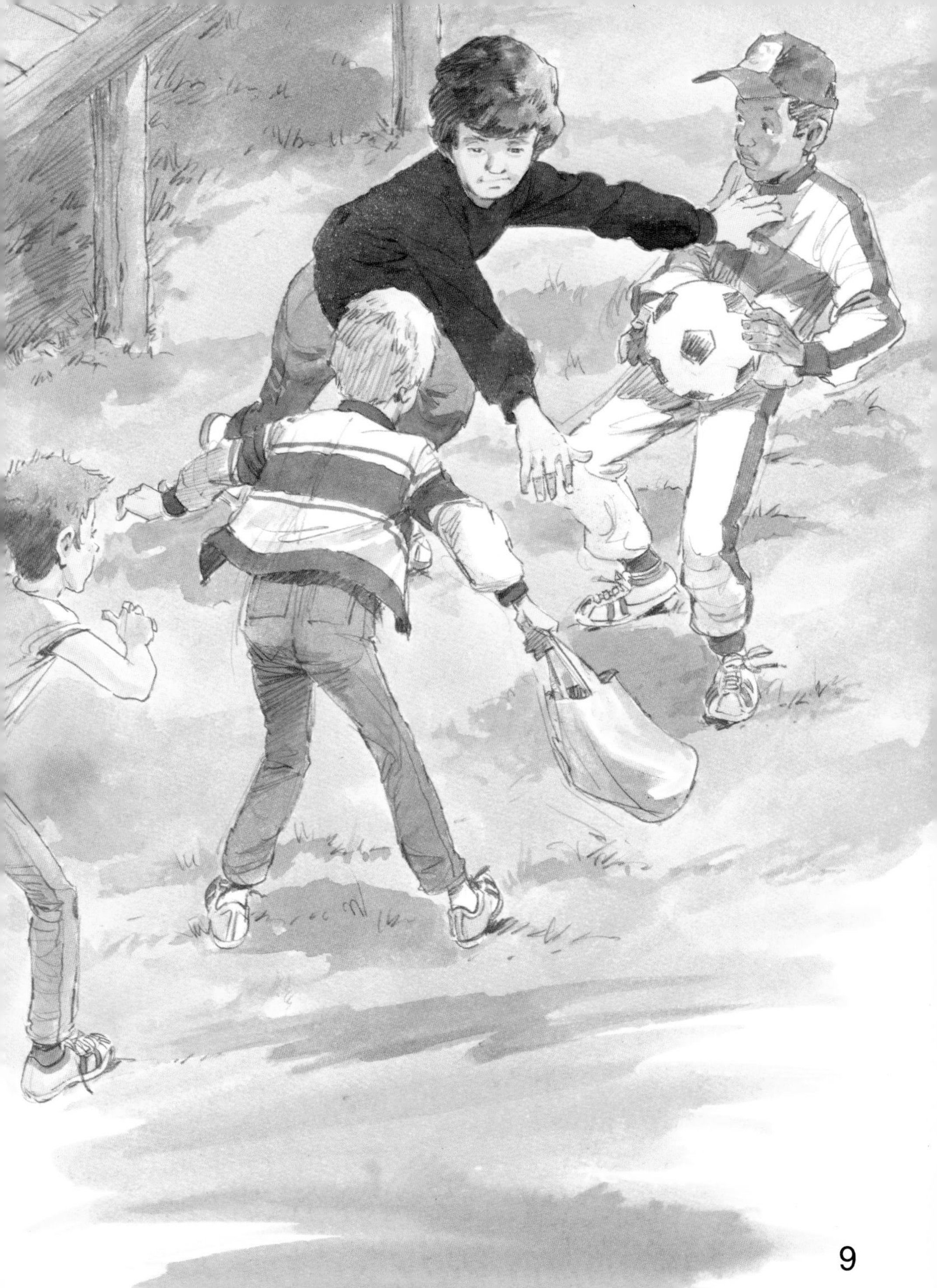

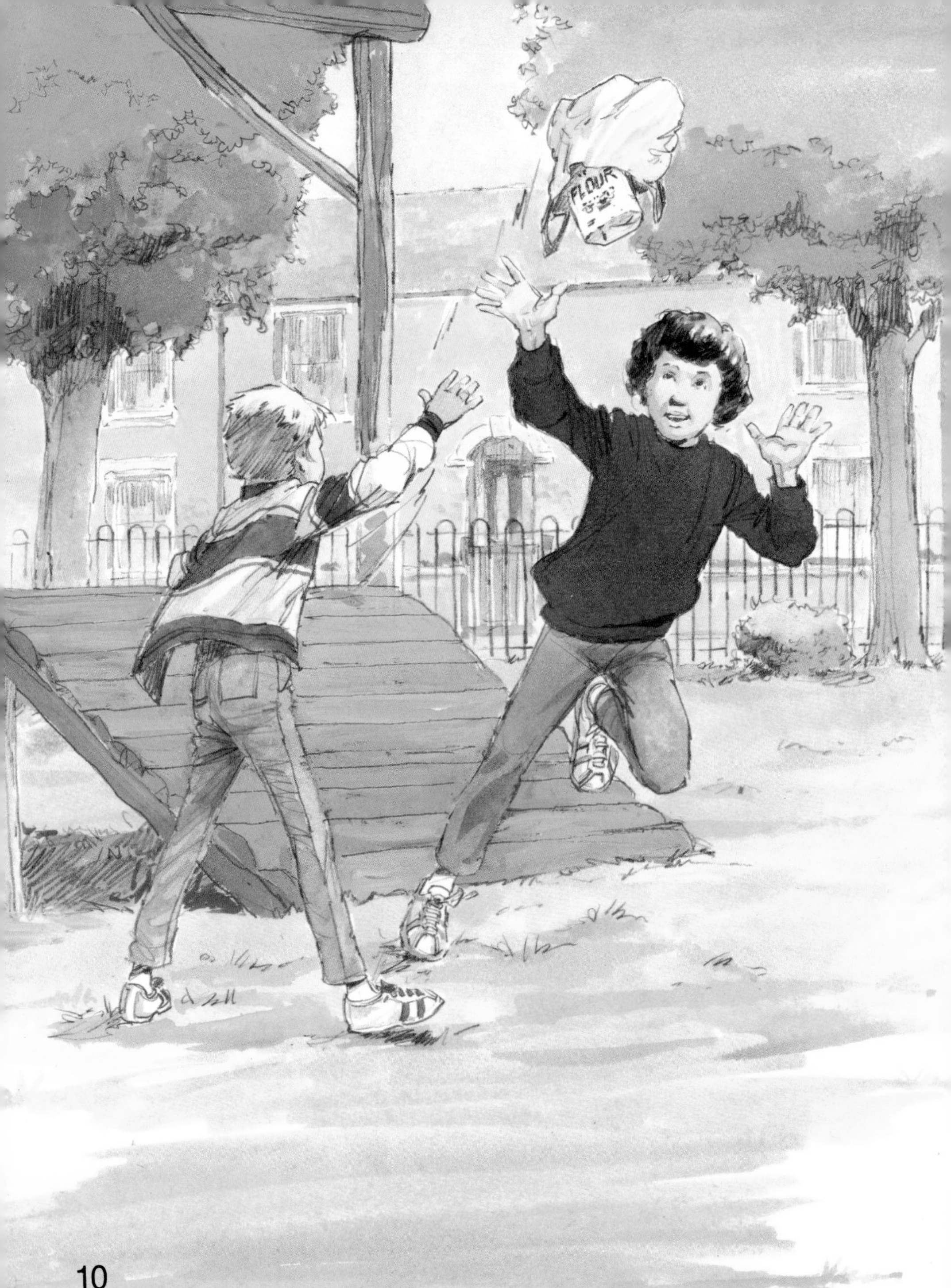
FLOUR

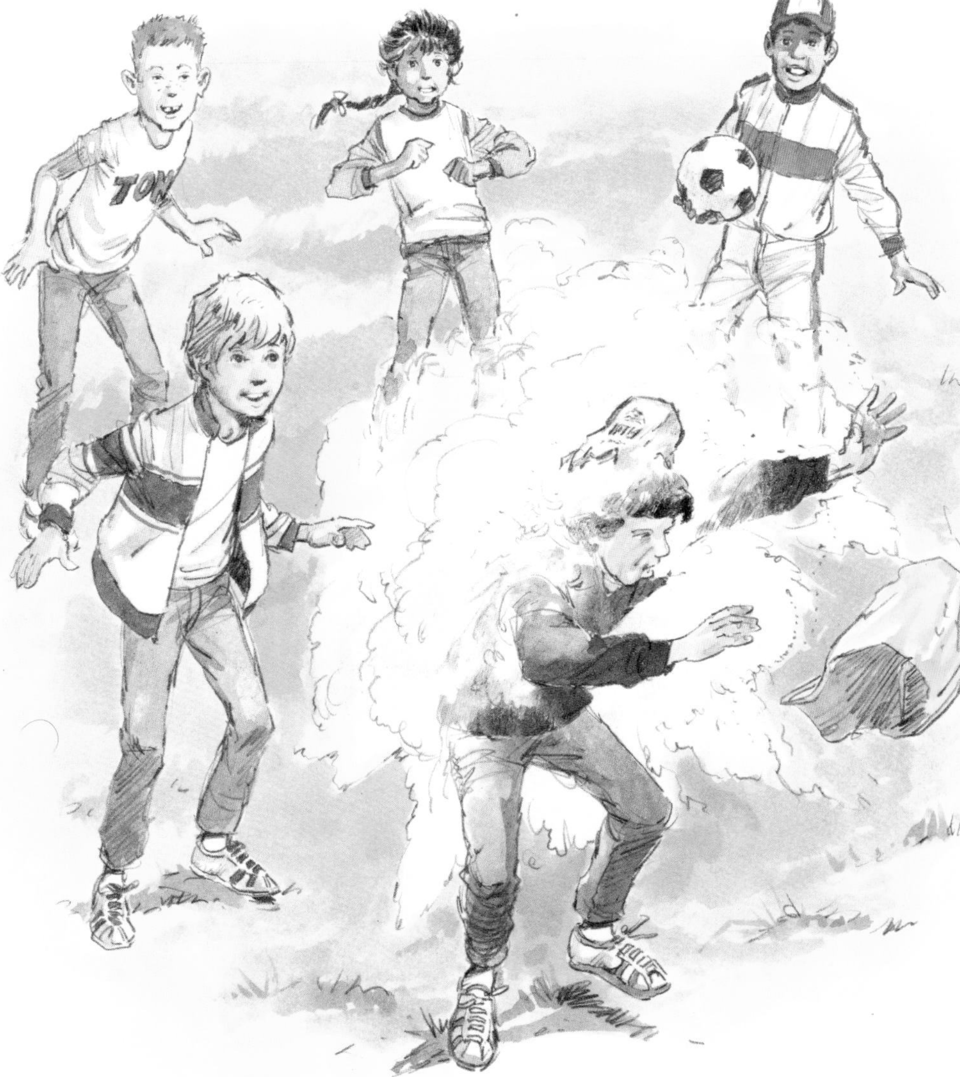

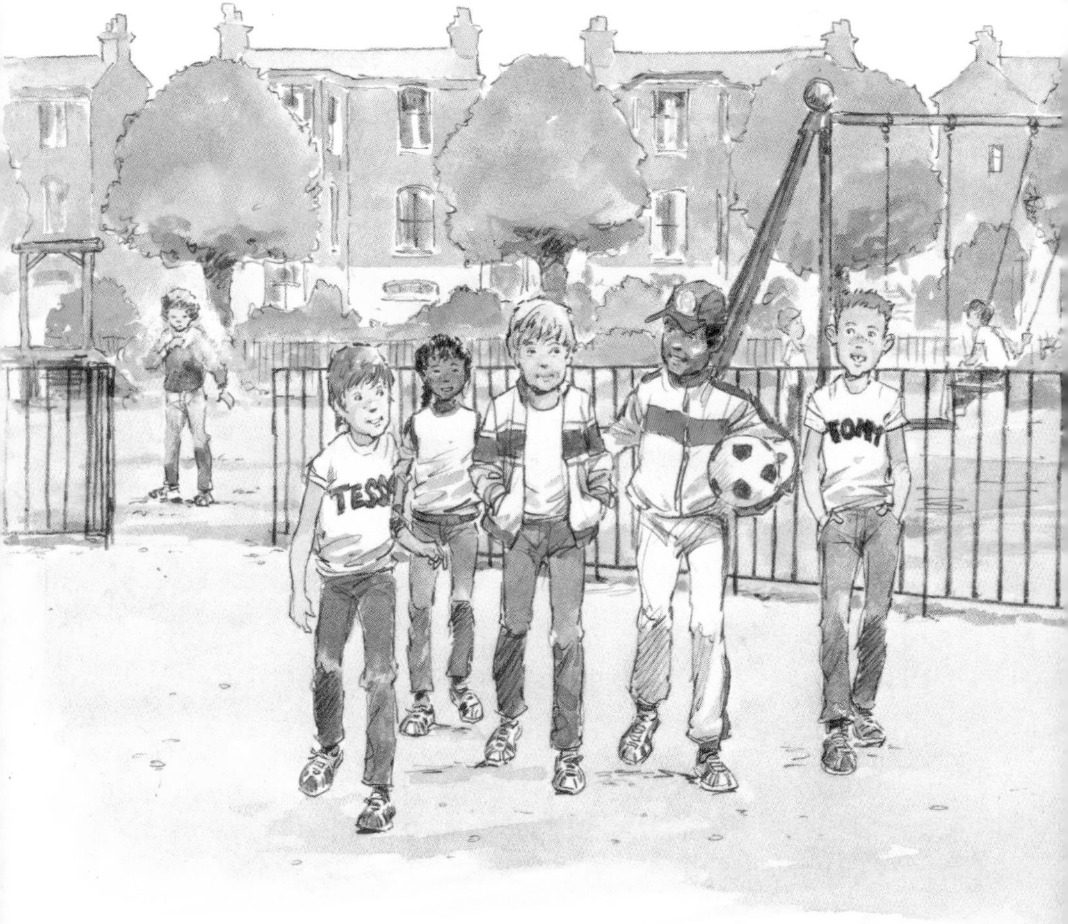
TESS
TOMY